JONAH

S0-CAB-638

JONAH

The complete text of Jonah from
The Holy Bible, New International Version

Illustrated by Kurt Mitchell
Foreword by Edith Schaeffer

CROSSWAY BOOKS • WESTCHESTER, ILLINOIS
A DIVISION OF GOOD NEWS PUBLISHERS

Published 1981 by Crossway Books,
a division of Good News Publishers,
9825 W. Roosevelt Road,
Westchester, Illinois 60153

Cover and interior illustrations
copyright © 1981 by Kurt Mitchell

The complete text of Jonah is from
the Holy Bible: New International Version
copyright © 1978 by New York International Bible Society.
Used by permission of Zondervan Bible Publishers
Grand Rapids, Michigan 49506, U.S.A.

All other portions of the text
copyright © 1981 by Good News Publishers
Westchester, Illinois 60153, U.S.A.

Concept and Design by Ray Cioni / *The Cioni Artworks*

All rights reserved. No part of this publication may be
reproduced, stored in a retrieval system or transmitted
in any form by any means, electronic, mechanical, photocopy,
recording, or otherwise, without the prior permission of
the publisher, except as provided in USA copyright law.

First printing, 1981

Printed in the United States of America

ISBN 0-89107-224-1

FOREWORD

This beautiful children's book is a remarkable achievement. The illustrations by artist Kurt Mitchell are truly good art and are reproduced here in brilliant, full page color plates. The book's designer, Ray Cioni, has carefully woven the text and illustrations together so that they speak simply and impressively to everyone. And the text—taken directly from the New International Version of the Bible—encourages children to begin reading the Bible for themselves, as they look at the pictures over mother or daddy's shoulder, or sit on grandmother or grandfather's lap while being read to. Adults, just as much as children, will enjoy the details of the fantastic pictures, discovering new facets of the drawings each time they read together. This is a children's book that will be passed down for generations, as long as the paper lasts.

In the Chronicles of Narnia, C. S. Lewis brought the reality of the supernatural alive to a generation of readers. Now this book with its text and drawings accomplishes a similar goal, bringing fresh understanding to the story of Jonah and the reality of God. In a new way, we sense the terror and disgust Jonah felt when he was asked to go preach to the enemy city of Nineveh. How vividly a mouse being sent to a city of cats, to bring a message from God, portrays the fear Jonah felt when he sailed off in a completely opposite direction from the one God had commanded. Many, many times in life we will identify with that mouse. And so will our children and grandchildren as they begin to have their eyes of understanding opened to the marvel of the teaching of God's Word.

The wonder of the Bible is that it is never out of date. The Word of God applies to each moment in history. Today as much as ever, our life and actions need to be based upon an understanding from God.

We parents, grandparents, aunts, and uncles can relate so often to Jonah as we look back over various moments in our own past history, or perhaps as we look at today's schedule. We can remember heading in the opposite direction mentally, if not physically—running away from a hard task which God has opened up for us to do, but which we don't want to do. It is important to impress upon our children that "we" are being spoken to in the Bible, rather than "you." All of us are under the teaching of God's Word. The story of Jonah is history which God has included in the Bible because of its vital importance to each of us. The very same reason which makes this history important in teaching children makes it important for us to review it over and over again.

Through Jonah, children need to discover, and we need to be reminded of, the marvelous compassion of God. God's compassion is so great that He sent one of His own believing Hebrew people to preach and urge the wicked unbelievers of Nineveh to repent and turn to Him. So often the false idea of a harsh God is given to children, as if this were "the Old Testament teaching." But here the contrast is so clear—between the loving compassion of God and the selfish cruel desire of Jonah to let the people of Nineveh be destroyed.

The reality of communicating with the living God is taught in Jonah in a splendid way. Jonah has not only run away from God, but now in the sea he is suddenly swallowed by the great fish. How far he is from God—not just physically, but in disobedience! Yet in the midst of the fish's insides, Jonah prays earnestly: "In my distress I called to the Lord, and he answered me. From the depths of the grave I called for help, and you listened to my cry." How often we feel shut away by "waves and darkness," realizing that we have in some measure been unfaithful to the direction God has given us. For ourselves as parents, and for our children and grandchildren, we find a thrilling picture of compassion as God accepts and answers Jonah's prayer—and as God lovingly rescues Jonah, sets his feet on a dry path, and points him firmly back to the place he has been sent before.

Another aspect of God's compassion is also here. As the little "mouse" goes on to the fearful "city of cats" and gives his message, we can see more clearly the meaning of weakness. God promises His strength in our weakness, so that we can do the tasks that are too great or impossible for us to do in our weakness. The story of Jonah illustrates both the extent of our weakness and the limits of our strength when we are called to stand and speak God's message in the midst of enemy territory. In a time when "self fulfillment," peace, and affluence are the only ideals, it is important to teach the lessons of God's Word which give an opposite ideal. It is possible to speak truth with courage when the "odds" are so terrific that one is in essence a mouse standing before cats. Yet we can have courage if we know that there is Someone who answers when we call upon Him, and will help us in representing Him.

When the people of Nineveh received God's wonderful message and turned to Him in repentance, God forgave them compassionately. But when Jonah saw this, he became enraged, even asking God to take his life! What an accurate picture this is of the sinfulness of human beings in their deep lack of compassion for others. God's lesson to Jonah is meant to be a lesson for not only children but for us.

The scene, especially as captured in Kurt Mitchell's illustrations, is so true to the way we carry on. Jonah goes out in the blazing desert sun, hoping that God will destroy Ninevah. When a green vine grows up making a cool shade, a sleek satisfaction comes to the "mouse's" face. (It's easy to picture ourselves sitting there with him, gloating in our own self-satisfaction.) Cool green shade shutting away the desert sun . . . How nice. But—God's lesson is pictured as we see the worm getting ready to destroy the vine and as a scorchingly hot wind is about to make life unbearable.

What is the lesson? Jonah had protection under the vine he had not made, nor even planted and watered—and yet he is so concerned about his own comfort that he is furious when the protection is removed. How then, asks God, can Jonah justify his desire to blot out God's concern about 120,000 people? Once more the potent contrast is being made between the dismal lack of compassion among human beings and God's compassionate call to us to "choose life" by turning to Him. This is the same compassion shown in Deuteronomy 30:15-20, where God is urging the Israelites to "choose life" in order that they and their children may live. That choice speaks of listening to God's voice, holding fast to Him, because "the Lord is your life." This teaching, in the midst of a humanistic flood of movies, magazines, TV shows, and books, cannot be too frequently reread and repeated. Nor can it be too vividly portrayed in order to help our children, and fortify ourselves, to know that "this God is our God" to whom we will be faithful all our lives. This is the one true living God of the Bible, the God of Abraham, Isaac, and Jacob. He is a God of love and compassion, who can be reached by prayer at any time, in any place, even by one of his children who is in the depths of the stormy waves.

Edith Schaeffer

JONAH

The word of the Lord came to Jonah son of Amittai: "Go to the great city of Nineveh and preach against it, because its wickedness has come up before me."

But Jonah ran away from the LORD and headed for Tarshish. He went down to Joppa, where he found a ship bound for that port. After paying the fare, he went aboard and sailed for Tarshish to flee from the LORD.

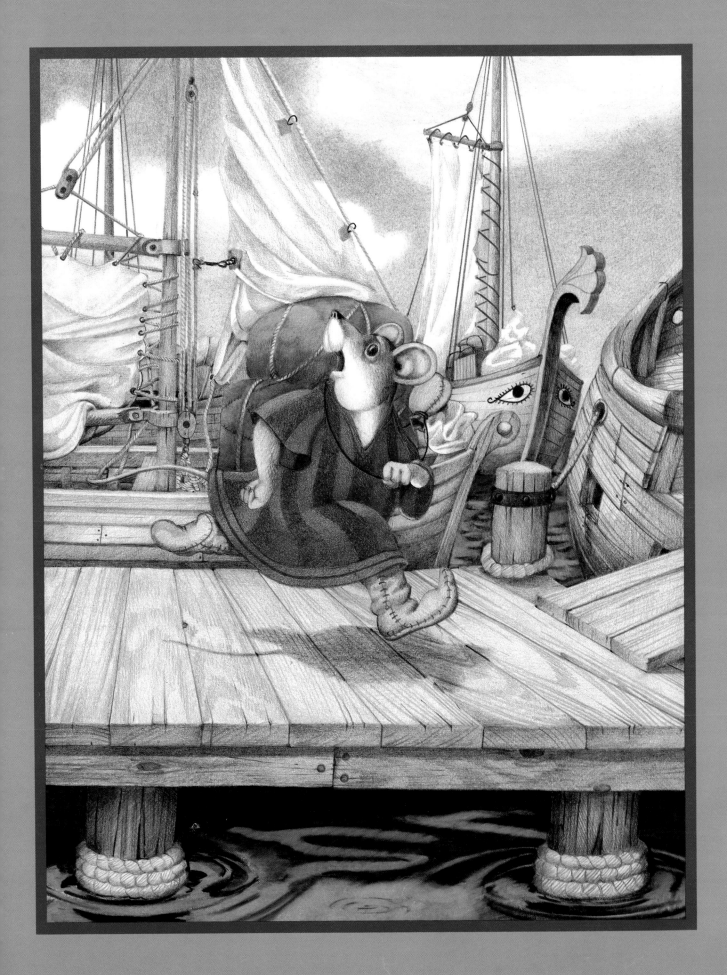

Then the LORD sent a great wind on the sea, and such a violent storm arose that the ship threatened to break up. All the sailors were afraid and each cried out to his own god. And they threw the cargo into the sea to lighten the ship.

But Jonah had gone below deck, where he lay down and fell into a deep sleep. The captain went to him and said, "How can you sleep? Get up and call on your god! Maybe he will take notice of us, and we will not perish."

Then the sailors said to each other, "Come, let us cast lots to find out who is responsible for this calamity." They cast lots and the lot fell on Jonah.

So they asked him, "Tell us, who is responsible for making all this trouble for us? What do you do? Where do you come from? What is your country? From what people are you?"

He answered, "I am a Hebrew and I worship the LORD, the God of heaven, who made the sea and the land."

This terrified them and they asked, "What have you done?" (They knew he was running away from the LORD, because he had already told them so.)

The sea was getting rougher and rougher. So they asked him, "What should we do to you to make the sea calm down for us?"

P ick me up and throw me into the sea," he replied, "and it will become calm. I know that it is my fault that this great storm has come upon you."

Instead, the men did their best to row back to land. But they could not, for the sea grew even wilder than before. Then they cried to the LORD, "O LORD, please do not let us die for taking this man's life. Do not hold us accountable for killing an innocent man, for you, O LORD, have done as you pleased." Then they took Jonah and threw him overboard, and the raging sea grew calm. At this the men greatly feared the LORD, and they offered a sacrifice to the LORD and made vows to him.

But the LORD provided a great fish to swallow Jonah, and Jonah was inside the fish three days and three nights.

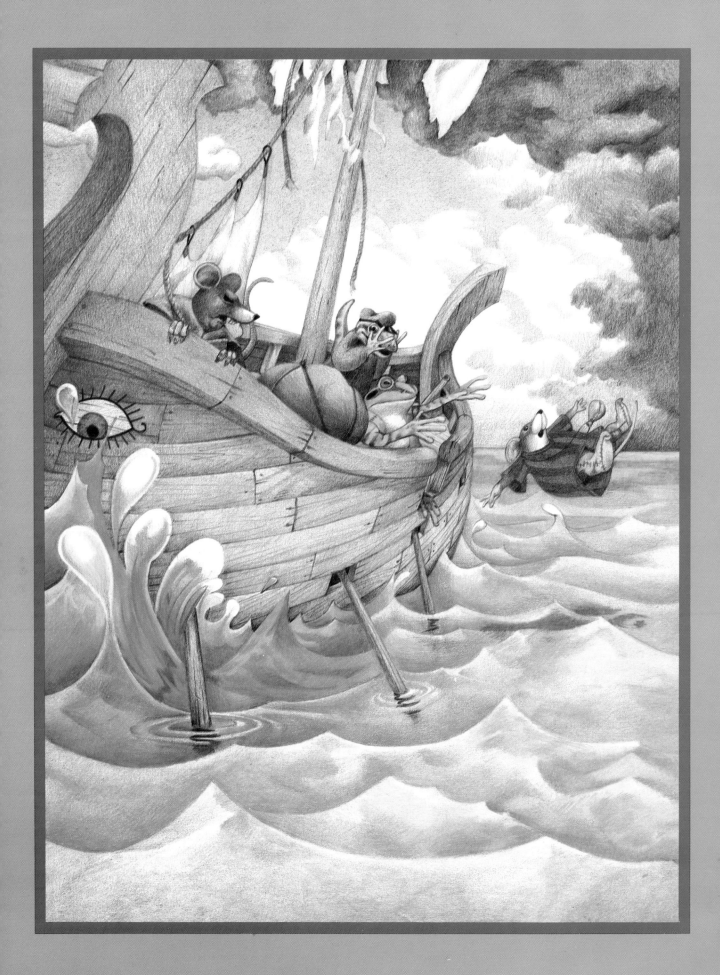

CHAPTER 2

From inside the fish
Jonah prayed to the LORD his God. He said:

"In my distress I called to the LORD,
   and he answered me.
From the depths of the grave I called for help,
   and you listened to my cry.
You hurled me into the deep,
   into the very heart of the seas,
   and the currents swirled about me;
all your waves and breakers
   swept over me.
I said, 'I have been banished
   from your sight;
yet I will look again
   toward your holy temple.'

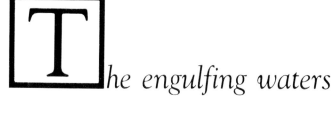he engulfing waters
threatened me,
the deep surrounded me;
seaweed was wrapped around my head.
To the roots of the mountains I sank down;
the earth beneath barred me in forever.
But you brought my life up from the pit,
O LORD my God.

"When my life was ebbing away,
I remembered you, LORD,
and my prayer rose to you,
to your holy temple.

"Those who cling to worthless idols
forfeit the grace that could be theirs.
But I, with a song of thanksgiving,
will sacrifice to you.
What I have vowed I will make good.
Salvation comes from the LORD."

And the LORD commanded the fish, and it
vomited Jonah onto dry land.

CHAPTER 3

T

hen the word of the LORD came to Jonah a second time: "Go to the great city of Nineveh and proclaim to it the message I give you."

Jonah obeyed the word of the LORD and went to Nineveh. Now Nineveh was a very large city; it took three days to go all through it.

J

onah started into the city, going a day's journey, and he proclaimed: "Forty more days and Nineveh will be destroyed." The Ninevites believed God. They declared a fast, and all of them, from the greatest to the least, put on sackcloth.

When the news reached the king of Nineveh, he rose from his throne, took off his royal robes, covered himself with sackcloth and sat down in the dust.

Then he issued a proclamation in Nineveh:

"By the decree of the king and his nobles:

Do not let any man or beast, herd or flock, taste anything; do not let them eat or drink. But let man and beast be covered with sackcloth. Let everyone call urgently on God. Let them give up their evil ways and their violence. Who knows? God may yet relent and with compassion turn from his fierce anger so that we will not perish.''

When God saw what they did and how they turned from their evil ways, he had compassion and did not bring upon them the destruction he had threatened.

CHAPTER 4

But Jonah was greatly displeased and became angry. He prayed to the LORD, "O LORD, is this not what I said when I was still at home? That is why I was so quick to flee to Tarshish. I knew that you are a gracious and compassionate God, slow to anger and abounding in love, a God who relents from sending calamity. Now, O LORD, take away my life, for it is better for me to die than to live."

But the LORD replied, "Have you any right to be angry?"

Jonah went out and sat down at a place east of the city. There he made himself a shelter, sat in its shade and waited to see what would happen to the city.

T hen the LORD God provided a vine and made it grow up over Jonah to give shade for his head to ease his discomfort, and Jonah was very happy about the vine. But at dawn the next day God provided a worm, which chewed the vine so that it withered. When the sun rose, God provided a scorching east wind, and the sun blazed on Jonah's head so that he grew faint. He wanted to die, and said, "It would be better for me to die than to live."

But God said to Jonah, "Do you have a right to be angry about the vine?"

"I do," he said. "I am angry enough to die."

But the LORD said, "You have been concerned about this vine, though you did not tend it or make it grow. It sprang up overnight and died overnight. But Nineveh has more than a hundred and twenty thousand people who cannot tell their right hand from their left, and many cattle as well. Should I not be concerned about that great city?"